Why Am I Here?

Written by
Gin Yu

Illustrated by
Aljon & Nova Inertia

I am here to give joy.

I am here to give meaning.

I am here to give peace.

I am here to give smiles.

I am here to give hope.

I am here to give hugs.

I am here to give kisses.

I am here to give comfort.

I am here to give effort.

I am here to give a cup of water.

I am here to give appreciation.

I am here to give ideas.

I am here to give forgiveness.

I am here to give friendship.

I am here to give prayers.

I am here to give my best.

I am here to give a hand.

I am here to give my word.

I am here to give my time.

I am here to give my attention.

I am here to give support.

I am here to give example.

I am here to give change.

I am here to give respect.

I am here to give praise.

I am here to give help.

I am here to give my gifts.

I am here
to give
patience.

I am here to give recognition.

I am here to give life.

I am here to give love.

I am here to give.

About the Author

Born in Taiwan, raised in Brazil, and currently living in Los Angeles, Gin Yu's journey defines her diverse identity. With a passion for telling stories, Gin balances economic acumen and creative passion as a TV & Film Producer and Author.

About the Illustrators

Aljon and Nova, "Team Inertia," are inspired to create beautiful, one-of-a-kind illustrations for children's books. Their work brings engagement to stories that speak to good morals and values while providing lessons for today's youth.

Their colorful illustrations bring life to the author's content so the words come alive on the pages. Aljon and Nova's extraordinary work is featured in children's books worldwide.

About the Publisher

Teresa Velardi founded Authentic Endeavors Publishing and the imprint, Book Endeavors. Blessed with numerous gifts and talents, Teresa's abilities as a writer, editor, publisher, and coach are vital ingredients she brings to those who choose to share their message with the world through her publishing platform.
AuthenticEndeavorsPublishing.com

Acknowledgments

Thank you to Simon Sinek, for giving me the inspiration.

Gratitude abounds to Teresa Velardi for her expertise in shaping this project. Special thanks to the talented Aljon and Nova Inertia, whose creativity brought these pages to life. Heartfelt appreciation to the entire team at Book Endeavors for their professionalism and enthusiasm. I am sincerely grateful for the opportunity to work with you—thank you for making this dream come true.

Last but not least, I would like to thank the Changs, my friends, and my family, whom I give to, but who have given me so much more.

Dedication

To all the givers in the world,
you make this world better.

ISBN: 978-1-955668-73-6 (paperback)
       978-1-955668-96-5 (hardback)
       978-1-955668-97-2 (ebook)
Library of Congress Control Number 2023924148

BOOK ENDEAVORS

Made in the USA
Columbia, SC
15 April 2024